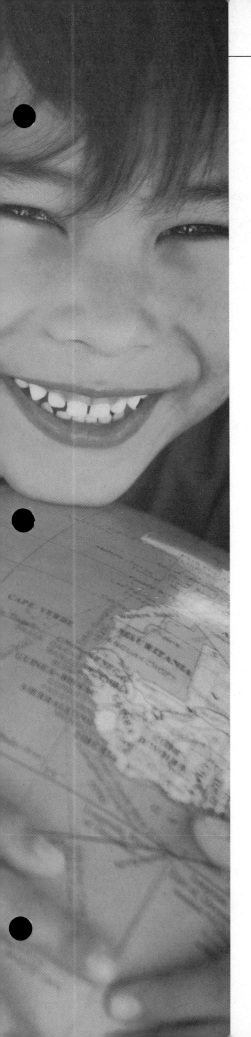

Social Studies Alive!®
Me and My World

TCi™

Chief Executive Officer
Bert Bower

Chief Operating Officer
Amy Larson

Director of Product Development
Maria Favata

Strategic Product Manager
Nathan Wellborne

Content Developer
Ginger Wu

Senior Strategic Editor
Kim Merlino

Program Editors and Writers
Mikaila Garfinkel
Sally Isaacs
Glenda Stewart
Kelly Stewart
Alex White
Ginger Wu

Production Manager
Jodi Forrest

Operations & Software Manager
Marsha Ifurung

Designer
Sarah Osentowski

Art Direction
Julia Foug

Teachers' Curriculum Institute
PO Box 1327
Rancho Cordova, CA 95741

Customer Service: 800-497-6138
www.teachtci.com

ISBN 978-1-58371-035-7
1 2 3 4 5 6 7 8 9 10 -DH- 20 19 18 17 16 15

Manufactured by Hess Print Solutions, Brimfield, OH
United States of America, July, 2015, Job 261152

Contents

1 Who Am I?

Preview 1

Reading Notes 2

Reading Further 6

Processing 8

2 What Is a Family?

Preview 9

Reading Notes 10

Reading Further 13

Processing 14

3 How Do I Get Along with Others?

Preview 15

Reading Notes 16

Reading Further 20

Processing 22

4 How Do I Make Friends?

Preview 23

Reading Notes 24

Reading Further 28

Processing 30

5 How Do I Solve Problems with Others?

Preview 31

Reading Notes 32

Reading Further 35

Processing 38

6 How Can I Be a Good Helper at School?

Preview 39

Reading Notes 40

Reading Further 44

Processing 46

7 What Is in My Neighborhood?

Preview 47

Reading Notes 48

Reading Further 52

Processing 54

8 Where Am I in the World?

Preview 55

Reading Notes 56

Reading Further 60

Processing 62

9 How Do People Live Around the World?

Preview 63

Reading Notes 64

Reading Further 67

Processing 69

10 What Do People Need and Want?

Preview 71

Reading Notes 72

Reading Further 75

Processing 76

11 How Can I Help Take Care of the World?

Preview 77

Reading Notes 78

Reading Further 83

Processing 84

Credits 85

Draw a self-portrait.

Draw how you look. Fill in the blanks.

I have _____.

I have _____.

In the heart, show who or what you care about.
Use pictures and words.

Draw a line to each feeling.

●   ● surprised

●   ● happy

●   ● sad

Show four things you can do.
Draw a picture in each square.

Draw a line to each person.

George Washington

Betsy Ross

With your class, recite the pledge.

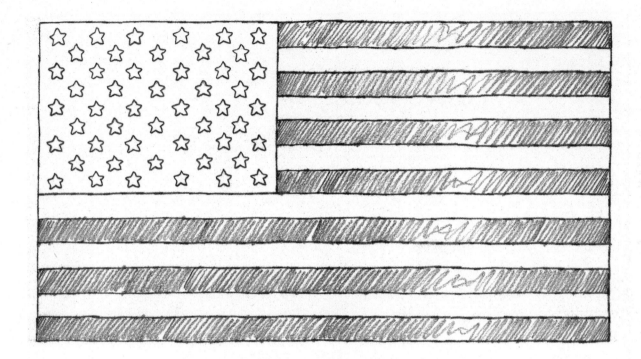

The Pledge of Allegiance

I pledge allegiance

to the Flag

of the United States of America,

and to the Republic

for which it stands,

one Nation, under God,

indivisible,

with liberty and justice for all.

Check the things that are true.

☐ I am special.

☐ I care.

☐ I have feelings.

☐ I can do many things.

Draw your family.

What activity does your family do together?
Use pictures and words to show it.

Put the family photos in order.

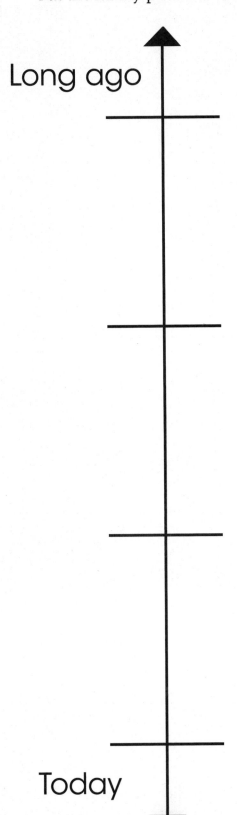

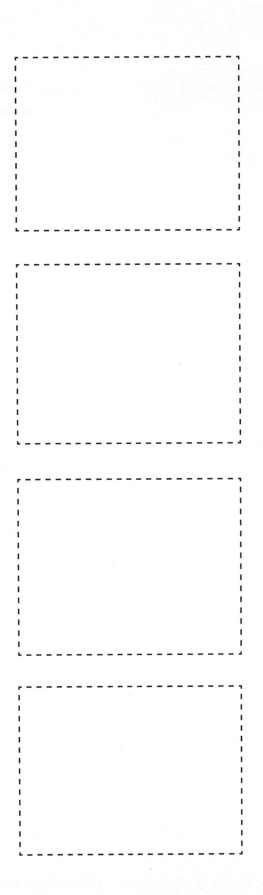

red — Circle your birthday.

blue — Circle the week before your birthday.

green — Circle the month after your birthday.

January

S	M	T	W	Th	F	S
				1	2	3
4	5	6	7	8	9	10
11	12	13	14	15	16	17
18	19	20	21	22	23	24
25	26	27	28	29	30	31

February

S	M	T	W	Th	F	S
1	2	3	4	5	6	7
8	9	10	11	12	13	14
15	16	17	18	19	20	21
22	23	24	25	26	27	28

March

S	M	T	W	Th	F	S
1	2	3	4	5	6	7
8	9	10	11	12	13	14
15	16	17	18	19	20	21
22	23	24	25	26	27	28
29	30	31				

April

S	M	T	W	Th	F	S
			1	2	3	4
5	6	7	8	9	10	11
12	13	14	15	16	17	18
19	20	21	22	23	24	25
26	27	28	29	30		

May

S	M	T	W	Th	F	S
					1	2
3	4	5	6	7	8	9
10	11	12	13	14	15	16
17	18	19	20	21	22	23
24	25	26	27	28	29	30
31						

June

S	M	T	W	Th	F	S
	1	2	3	4	5	6
7	8	9	10	11	12	13
14	15	16	17	18	19	20
21	22	23	24	25	26	27
28	29	30				

July

S	M	T	W	Th	F	S
			1	2	3	4
5	6	7	8	9	10	11
12	13	14	15	16	17	18
19	20	21	22	23	24	25
26	27	28	29	30	31	

August

S	M	T	W	Th	F	S
						1
2	3	4	5	6	7	8
9	10	11	12	13	14	15
16	17	18	19	20	21	22
23	24	25	26	27	28	29
30	31					

September

S	M	T	W	Th	F	S
		1	2	3	4	5
6	7	8	9	10	11	12
13	14	15	16	17	18	19
20	21	22	23	24	25	26
27	28	29	30			

October

S	M	T	W	Th	F	S
				1	2	3
4	5	6	7	8	9	10
11	12	13	14	15	16	17
18	19	20	21	22	23	24
25	26	27	28	29	30	31

November

S	M	T	W	Th	F	S
1	2	3	4	5	6	7
8	9	10	11	12	13	14
15	16	17	18	19	20	21
22	23	24	25	26	27	28
29	30					

December

S	M	T	W	Th	F	S
		1	2	3	4	5
6	7	8	9	10	11	12
13	14	15	16	17	18	19
20	21	22	23	24	25	26
27	28	29	30	31		

Draw a line to each picture.

Thomas
Jefferson ● ●

U.S.
Flag ● ●

Fourth of
July ● ●

Declaration
of
Independence ● ●

Draw a picture to show your birthday plans.
Show a family tradition.

On My Next Birthday

Are these children getting along?
Circle thumbs-up or thumbs-down.

What kind of speaking voice should you use?
Draw a line to match.

whisper ●   ●

presenting to the class

talk quietly ●   ●

working in a group

speak up ●   ●

watching a movie

Draw a picture of a good listener.

Draw a picture of you and your friends taking turns.

Which are good choices?
Circle the pictures.

I Make Good Choices

Draw a picture of a rule at school.
Write the rule below your picture.

_____

_____

Draw a picture of a rule at home.
Write the rule below your picture.

Show that you will try to get along with others.
Sign the contract below.

I promise to get along.
- I will talk.
- I will listen.
- I will take turns.
- I will make good choices.

_____

Draw a friend.
Write your friend's name.

_____ is my friend.

How do you introduce yourself to a new friend?
Draw a picture. Write your name.

I Can Introduce Myself

Hello, my name
is _____.
What is yours?

How do you ask a friend to play?
Draw a picture. Write what you would like to do.

I Can Ask a Friend to Play

Circle the pictures that show children sharing.

I Can Share

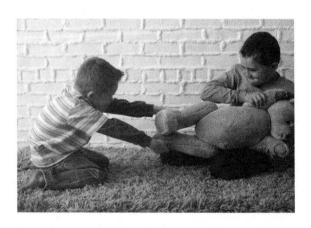 

Draw a picture of a kind action.

Kind Action

How was Squanto a friend to the Pilgrims?
Circle the answer.

Squanto taught the Pilgrims how to grow _____.

oranges

corn

How were the Pilgrims friends to the Wampanoags?
Circle the answer.

The Pilgrims shared _____.

food

trees

Retell the story in order.
Number the events from 1 to 4.

☐ The next spring, Squanto helped the Pilgrims plant corn.

☐ That fall, the Pilgrims and Wampanoags shared a special feast.

☐ All summer, the Pilgrims worked hard.

☐ In winter, the Pilgrims came to American.

Draw a picture to show how a new friend can help you.
Complete the sentence. Tell about your picture.

Friends Can Help Us

My new friend helps me _____

_____

_____.

How does it feel to have hurt feelings?
Draw a picture. Circle the word.

I feel _____.   happy   sad

Match the problem solving step with its picture.

Step 1
I stop, calm down.

●   ●

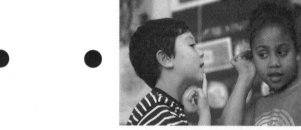

Step 2
I talk and listen.

●   ●

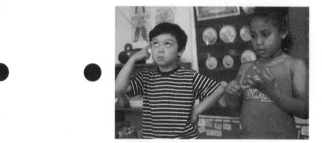

Step 3
I think of ways to
solve the problem.

●   ●

Step 4
I agree on a plan
and try it.

●   ●

How does our class like to calm down?
Write the number of votes. Circle the
way that got the most votes.

_____
votes

_____
votes

_____
votes

_____
votes

_____
votes

Show how Buddy can calm down.
Use pictures and words or numbers.

What job does each person have?
Match the job name to the person.

police officer ●

●

doctor ●

●

bus driver ●

● (photo)

teacher ●

●

What does each person do in his or her job?
Match the person to how he or she helps us.

teacher

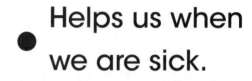

Helps us when
we are sick.

police officer

Drives us to
school.

doctor

Keeps us safe.

bus driver

Helps us learn.

Who else helps us?
Draw a picture. Complete the sentence.

A _____ helps us

_____.

Put the problem solving steps in order.
Number them from 1 to 4.

  I agree on a plan and try it.

  I talk and listen.

  I think of ways to solve the problem.

  I stop, calm down.

Circle the pictures that show
a handy helper.

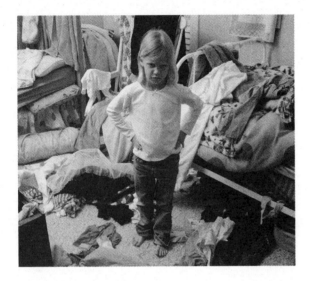

Are you a handy helper?   yes   no

Have your partner trace your hand.
Draw one way you help in class.
Complete the sentence.

I Am a Handy Helper

I am a handy helper when _____

_____.

What things can we take care of in
our classroom? Draw a picture.
Complete the sentence.

Taking Care of Things

We can take care of _____

_____.

Trace each shape. Then draw
each shape in the box.

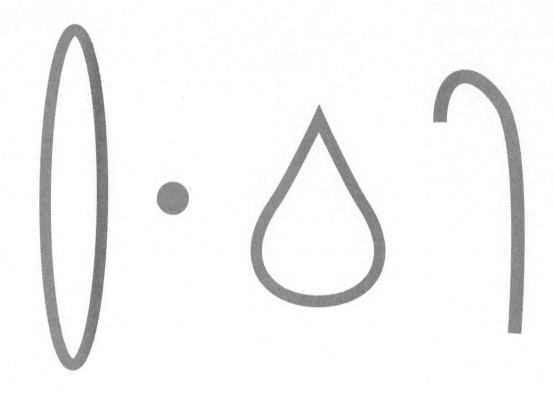

Listen carefully and follow the
teacher's directions.

I see _____.

Trace Bob's path on the map.

A School Map

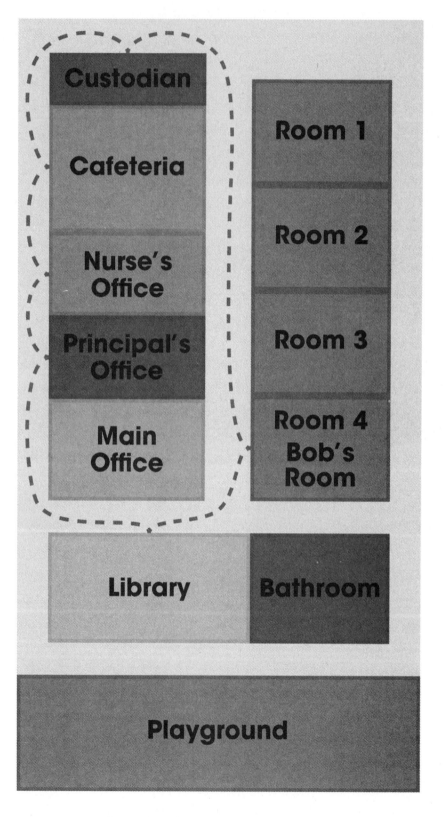

How does each person help?
Match the person to his or her job.

School Librarian

School Nurse

Custodian

Teacher

Helps us when we are hurt.

Helps us learn.

Helps us find books.

Helps keep the school clean.

How can you can be a good helper
at school? Fill in the blanks.

I can _____

of the class pet.

I can help keep the

class _____.

I can do my _____.

I can follow _____.

Word Bank
clean   directions   take care   work

Draw where you live.

Where I Live

What buildings are in a neighborhood?
Match the building with its name.

●   ● **police station**

●   ● **hospital**

●   ● **fire station**

●   ● **airport**

Circle what you would find in an outdoor place.

Look at the map key.

Color the land. green

Color the water. blue

Color the roads. black

Complete the sentences.

Map Key

Land

Water

Roads

Neighborhood Map

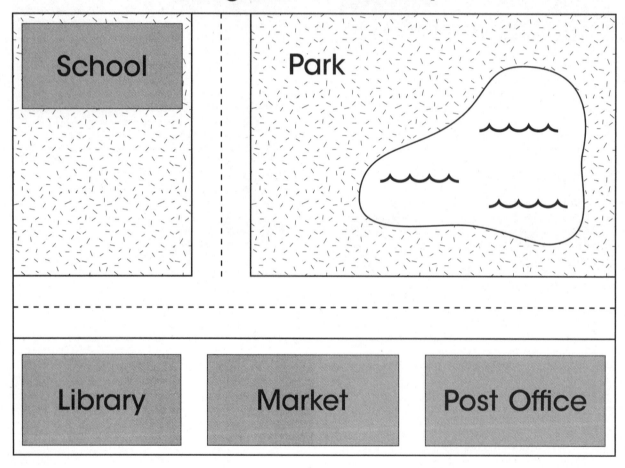

School

Park

Library

Market

Post Office

The library is left of the _____.

The school is near the _____.

Look at the class model of a
neighborhood. Draw a map
of your section. Show the
buildings and outdoor places.
Add a map key.

Map Key

Land

Water

Roads

Neighborhood Map

Write the words that tell about
Martin Luther King Jr.

Martin Luther King Jr.

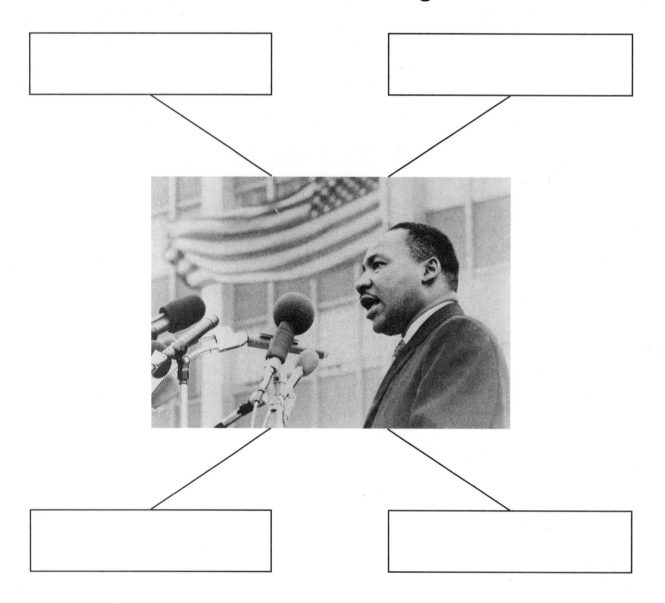

Word Bank

brave   fair   peaceful

strong   unfair   weak

Martin Luther King Jr. had a dream that
all people would be treated the same.
Draw a picture of your dream.
Complete the sentence.

My Dream...

I have a dream _____

_____.

Think about your real neighborhood.
Draw a picture of your favorite part.
Complete the sentence.

What I Like About My Neighborhood

My favorite part of my neighborhood is

_____

_____.

Mark all the places where you live.

☐ in a family

☐ in a neighborhood

☐ in a city

☐ in a state

☐ in a country

☐ in the world

Write the name of our city.
Draw a picture of something you like
about our city. Then draw yourself.

My City

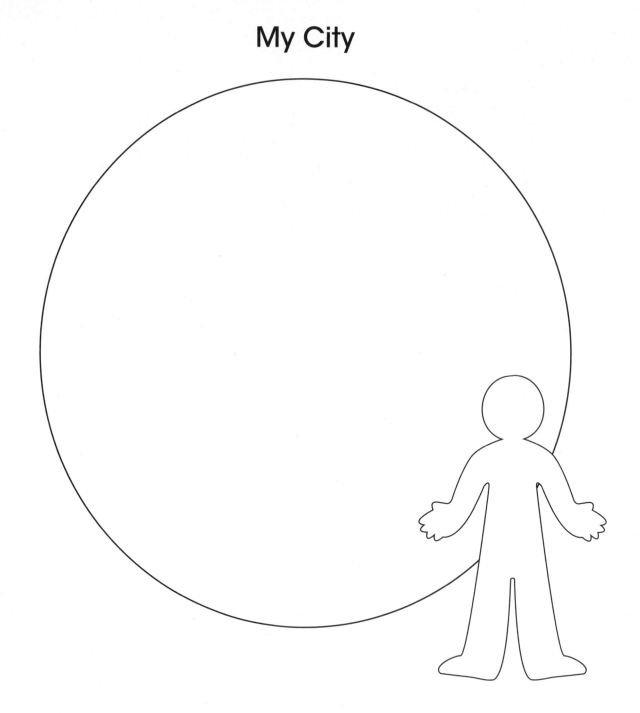

I live in a city called

_____

Write the name of our state.
Draw a picture of something you like
about our state. Then draw yourself.

My State

I live in a state called

_____.

Trace the letters that spell the name of our country. Draw a picture of something you like about our country. Then draw yourself.

My Country

I live in a country called the

_____ United States _____ of America.

Sketch the world inside the circle.

Color the land.

Color the water.

Then draw yourself.

My World

I live in the world.

Which pictures show symbols of our
country? Circle them.

Draw a picture of your favorite symbol of
our country. Complete the sentence.

My Favorite U.S. Symbol

My favorite U.S. symbol is

_____.

Write the name of the country. Circle
your state. Make a dot for your city.

A Map of the _____

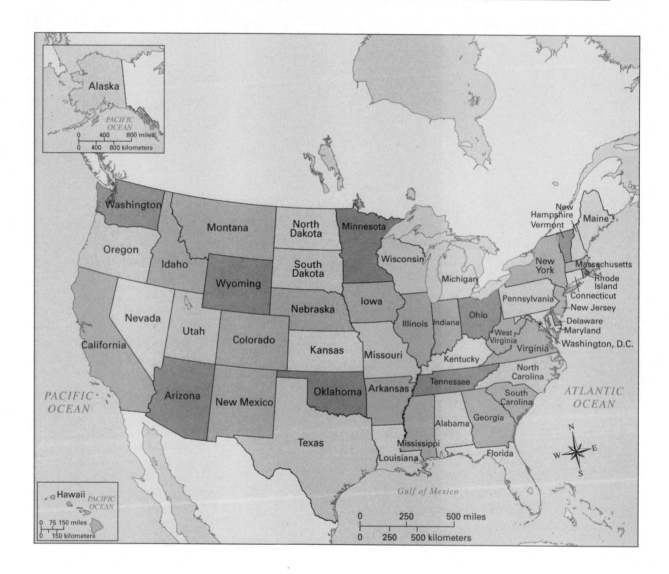

Draw a picture of something
you do during the day. Write
what you do.

I _____ .

Match the greeting with the language.

●   ● English

●   ● Spanish

●   ● Japanese

●   ● Arabic

Show one way you learned to write hello. _____

What are some items people around the
world use to eat? Circle two pictures.

What are some games children around
the world play? Circle two pictures.

Which picture matches the sentence?
Circle it.

People all over the world like music.

People all over the world follow laws.

Look at each item. Is the item used now
or was it used more often in the past?
Circle **now** or **then**.

now   then

now   then

now   then

now   then

Draw a picture for each sentence.

People around the world talk.

People around the world learn.

Draw a picture for each sentence.

People around the world eat.

People around the world play.

Draw a picture for each sentence.

People around the world like music.

People around the world follow laws.

Draw something you need.
Finish the sentence.

I need this because _____

_____.

Draw lines to where you see
food, clothing, and shelter.

clothing

shelter

food

Look at this picture. Then answer the questions.

What would you eat here? Circle it.

What would you wear here? Circle it.

Which house would you live in? Circle it.

What Do People Need and Want? **73**

On the left, show two needs. On
the right, show two wants.
Use pictures or words.

needs	wants

You have $10.
Which shirt would you buy? Circle it.

I chose this shirt because _____

_____.

How does your family meet your needs?
Draw a picture. Label it.

Where do you think your garbage goes? Draw a picture.

Where My Garbage Goes

Cut out The Garbage Story Cards.
Glue them in order. Retell the story to
a friend.

1

2

3

4

Match each piece of garbage to the
recycling bin where it goes.

Garbage

Recycling Bin

●

●

Paper

●

●

Cans

●

●

Glass

●

●

Plastic

Match each piece of garbage to what
it can be recycled into.

Garbage

New Product

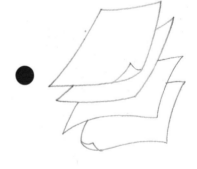

Circle one of the pieces of garbage. Draw a picture of how you could reuse it.

Look at each pair of items for sale on your handout. Circle the one you think will cut down on waste. Cut out the items. Glue them in the shopping cart.

What if you had one dollar?
Would you spend it or save it?

Draw the coins you would spend.
Draw the coins you would save.

spend   save

Finish the sentence. Then draw a
picture to show your promise.

I promise to help
make the world a
better place by

_____.

© Teachers' Curriculum Institute

Cover and Title Page:
Thinkstock

Lesson 1

6: MPVHistory/Alamy

Lesson 2

13T: Stocktrek Images, Inc./Alamy
13TC: Library of Congress
13BC: Getty Images
13B: Thomas Lozinski/Dreamstime

Lesson 3

15T: JGI/Jamie Grill/Blend
Images/Corbis
15C: Lyubov Kobyakova/ Dreamstime
15B: KidStock/Blend Images/Corbis
15R: Shutterstock
16T: Thinkstock
16C: iStockphoto
16B: Losevsky Pavel/Alamy
19TL: iStockphoto
19TR: Thinkstock
19CL: iStockphoto
19CR: Thinkstock
19BL: Thinkstock
19BR: Thinkstock

Lesson 4

26TL: Wong Sze Yuen/Dreamstime
26TR: 22tomtom/Dreamstime
26CL: Olga Bogatyrenko/Dreamstime
26CR: iStockphoto
26BL: iStockphoto
26BR: Thinkstock
28TL: Álvaro Germán Vilela/Dreamstime
28TR: Thinkstock
28BL: GL Archive/Alamy
28BR: North Wind Picture Archives/Alamy
29T: Shutterstock
29TC: Shutterstock
29BC: Shutterstock
29B: Shutterstock

Lesson 5

35-36T: Erik Isakson/Tetra Images/Corbis
35-36TC: Getty Images
35-36BC: Thinkstock
35-36B: Thinkstock

Lesson 6

39TL: iStockphoto
39BL: Thinkstock
45T: Fancy Collection/Superstock
45TC: David Buffington/Exactostock-1598/
Superstock
45BC: Thinkstock
45B: iStockphoto
46T: iStockphoto
46TC: iStockphoto
46BC: Thinkstock
46B: iStockphoto

Lesson 7

48T: Thinkstock
48TC: Nils Versemann/Dreamstime
48BC: Thinkstock
48B: Publicimage/Dreamstime
49TL: iStockphoto
49TR: Ed Flasza/Dreamstime
49CL: Thinkstock
49CR: Jan Wachala/Dreamstime
49BL: iStockphoto
49BR: Elena Elisseeva/Dreamstime
52: Library of Congress

Lesson 8

60TL: Image Source/GettyImages
60TR: Mrcmos/Dreamstime
60BL: Thinkstock
60BR: Michael Ventura/Alamy

Lesson 9

64T: Hughstoneian/Dreamstime
64TC: Jedimaster/Dreamstime
64BC: Itani / Alamy
64B: Pahham/Dreamstime
65TL: iStockphoto
65TR: iStockphoto
65TC: iStockphoto
65BC: iStockphoto
65BL: iStockphoto
65BR: iStockphoto
66TL: Vachiraphan Phangphan/Dreamstime
66TR: Greatstock Photographic Library/Alamy
66TC: iStockphoto
67BC: Cleardesign/Dreamstime
66BL: Thinkstock
66BR: iStockhoto
67T: Adams Picture Library t/a apl/Alamy
67TC: Sergey Rasulov/Dreamstime
67B: William Gottlieb/Corbis

Lesson 10

72: David Snyder/Dreamstime
73T: Erectus/Dreamstime
73TCL: Johnfoto/Dreamstime
73TCR: ynoclub/Dreamstime
73BCL: Thinkstock
73BCR: Thinkstock
73BL: Pavel Svoboda/
Dreamstime
73BR: Hel080808/Dreamstime
75: Thinkstock